Make a New Friend in Je

PassAlong Arch® Books help you s
Jesus with friends close to you and
children all around the world!

When you've enjoyed this story, pass it
along to a friend.   When your friend is fin-
ished, mail this book to the address below. Concordia Gospel
Outreach promises to deliver your book to a boy or girl some-
where in the world to help him or her learn about Jesus.

Myself

My name _____

My address _____

_____

My PassAlong Friend

My name _____

My address _____

_____

When you're ready to give
your PassAlong Arch® Book to a
new friend who doesn't know
about Jesus, mail it to

Concordia Gospel Outreach
3547 Indiana Avenue
St. Louis, MO 63118

PassAlong Series

God's Good Creation
Noah's Floating Zoo
Baby Moses' River Ride
Jonah's Fishy Adventure
Baby Jesus, Prince of Peace
Jesus Stills the Storm
Jesus' Big Picnic
God's Easter Plan

Presented to

LAUREN BOWN

LEAGUE OF

CHURCH LOYALTY

1999

NATIONAL CHRISTIAN EDUCATION COUNCIL
TEL: 0121 4724242

Jesus' Big Picnic

John 6:1–13 for Children

Carol Greene
Illustrated by Michelle Dorenkamp

CPH™
SAINT LOUIS

hen I was just a little lad,
I liked to wander free
Down in the town or through the hills
To see what I could see.

My mother always packed a lunch
To get me through the day.
"Be home by dark. Be careful and
Have fun," she'd always say.

Out on my own, I'd look at things
Around me, over, under.
And when I saw some special thing,
I'd sit down and I'd wonder.

Who taught that purple bird its song?
How does that spider spin?
Are beetles happy under rocks?
And why are worms so thin?

"Looks like a happy beetle to me."

I wondered about people too.
Why were so many sad
Or crabby when I asked them things?
Why couldn't they be glad?

And then one day I heard about
A special sort of Man,
So special that I told myself,
"I'll find Him if I can."

"I don't like crabby people."

His name is Jesus," people said.
   "He's healed many sick.
   Some say He is the Son of God.
   Some say a lunatic.

   "He's down beside the sea," they said,
   "Not very far away."
   "The Son of *God*?" My heart beat fast.
   "I'm going there today."

Me too!

I ran as fast as if I had
Grown wings upon my feet.
When lunchtime came, I didn't
Even want to stop and eat.

The Son of God would surely know
Those things that made me wonder.
Do trees talk to each other and
Do angel drums make thunder?

"Pant,
pant!"

And then I saw Him on a hill
With other men around.
I felt a little shy, so I
Crept up without a sound.

I crept till I was very close.
They didn't notice me.
Instead, they talked about a crowd
Of people by the sea.

"shhhh!"

N ow, Philip," Jesus said and smiled,
   "That's quite a crowd to feed.
   This place is lonely. Tell Me where
   To find the bread we'll need."

"*Bread*?" said Philip, and his face
   Turned redder than a beet.
   "Why, forty dollars wouldn't buy
   Enough for them to eat."

"Did someone say eat?"

I looked at Jesus sitting there.
His smile had mischief in it.
Oh, silly Philip! *I* would not
Doubt Jesus for a minute.

My mom had packed a good-sized lunch—
Five loaves and two small fishes.
My stomach growled and all at once
I thought it looked delicious.

I knew that I could eat it all,
But that was not my plan.
"Please give my lunch to Jesus," I
Said to a nearby man.

"This boy gave me his lunch," the man
Told Jesus with a frown.
"It isn't much." But Jesus said,
"Now sit the people down."

At least five thousand people sat
Upon that grassy hill.
As Jesus thanked God for my lunch,
They waited, tense and still.

And Jesus gave the people food.
He gave them more, and then,
When I thought it must all be gone,
He gave them some again.

"This is incredible!"

Each person had enough to eat.
(Oh, yes, I had some too.)
And when we'd leaned back, full as full,
What did that Jesus do?

He told His helpers to get up.
"Collect what's left," He said.
And when they did, they had twelve
baskets
Brimming full of bread.

"I'm so full!"

This *is* God's Son, I thought. I've met
The Son of God today.
He made my lunch a miracle.
Oh, what will Mother say?

But then the crowd began to talk,
Their voices like a hum.
"This Jesus person—it is He,
The One who was to come."

"What are they muttering about?"

He is the prophet long foretold,
Who will our freedom bring.
He'll drive the tyrants from our land.
Come on! Let's make Him king!"

But Jesus knew what they would do
And so He slipped away.
"I'm not that sort of king, My friends,"
I thought I heard Him say.

Then I got up and hurried home,
And as I ran, I thought,
I hadn't asked Him any of
The questions that I'd brought.

But still I knew that all was well,
And deep inside a spark
Of love for Jesus grew and burned.
(I made it home by dark.)

All that was many years ago.
I heard that Jesus died
Upon a cruel cross one day.
When I heard that, I cried.

But then God raised Him up, they say.
They say it was God's plan
To save us. Now I wonder at
The love of that God-Man.